New Woman®

presents

BEST CARTOONS

from

New Woman®

Compiled by Margaret Harold

"Not shaving your legs doesn't make you a New Woman,
Valerie. It makes you a hairy woman."

Published by New Woman, Inc.

Fort Worth, Texas

"You've got to learn to relax."

"She gave Freddie Knudson an enema."

"Oh, I could stand the heat, but I got out of the kitchen anyway and put that ability to better use."

"I stayed in a rotten marriage for two years because I didn't want to hurt my parents. Now, *they're* getting a divorce."

"I'd like to seek a second opinion. I'm sure you understand."

"Melvin, I am self-supporting, articulate and have never spit on you. So why do you call me 'baby'?"

"Do you know any music to close a deal by?"

"I met the most interesting person at my Self-Discovery class tonight—ME!"

"I'm thick—and tired of it."

"Now, *you* get them ready. *I'll* go out and blow the horn!"

"Shirley, what exactly do you mean when you say
that our marriage 'stinks'?"

"Go suck 1,000-year-old egg, most honorable master."

"I'm going home to Mommy!"

"I'm not interested in saving my marriage. I'm
interested in getting a divorce and saving my sanity!"

"This is labor. You want to speak to management."

"My last husband and I had two happy years together. Unfortunately, we were married for ten."

"You're going to make someone a good husband."

"My youthful figure is what I want to get *rid* of!"

"We're celebrating the fact that our judgment was astute enough to tell us that we're all wrong for each other."

"I'm so embarrassed! I'm the only kid on the block whose parents haven't outgrown each other."

"Don't be silly. The government has made job discrimination impossible. The law says you're not required to tell me if you're a man or a woman."

"Mind if I cut in?"

"If farmers can get paid for not growing crops,
it seems we should get a subsidy for not having kids."

"Marriage? And break up a beautiful friendship?"

"According to the marriage test in this magazine,
we shouldn't even know each other."

"The world hasn't changed much. Forty years ago I
married my boss, and now my grandson is marrying his!"

"She's always been 'lucky in love.' She's 35 and still single."

"Up with your hands or I'll shoot!"

"You're going to meet a fascinating woman —
the inner you!"

"I decided that since I was going to take the time to teach her to talk, I may as well have her say something worthwhile!"

"Dear Dean Martin: It has come to my attention that there is a serious misconception in the lyrics of your popular hit 'You're Nobody 'Til Somebody Loves You.' Unless you want to spend the remainder of your career sounding like a turkey, I suggest you change the song to 'You're Nobody 'Til You Love Yourself'!"

"I'll show you mine if you'll show me yours… provided of course, we can *find* them."

"If I had known we were going to have to live with your mother, George, I wouldn't have married you."

"Let's be honest, gorgeous—self-love is blind, too."

"No, I wouldn't like to go to your apartment to see your etchings. Would you like to come to my studio and buy some of mine?"

"I'm sorry. I can't bear to watch her degrade herself that way."

"Before women's equality, you would never have had the opportunity to be a bum."

"Polly wants to invest in crackers!"

"Mr. Nelson, when I said I wanted to see you *hustle,* I meant..."

"If I'm overqualified, why don't you just
raise your standards?"

"The choice for the presidency was between
Harry Melville and myself. He was the
best man for the job, but I
was the best person."

"Momma, wait 'till you meet Doris!
She's got everything I ever wanted in a woman —
charm, compassion, upward mobility . . ."

"How stereotypical!"

"My daughters-in-law."

"No, it doesn't bother me that my wife makes more than I
do. She also makes more than you."

"It's your mother. She's recalling you due to
manufacturing defects."

"I was on one of those water diets once, and gained
five gallons!!!"

"Very nice to meet you. What does your wife do?"

"...as president of the catering firm, I'd like to bring up the matter of overdue bills from your last three affairs!"

"Ring around the collar? Tell it to HIM—
HE does the laundry."

"With you, it's always early to bed and *nothing* to rise."

"You've been watching the soaps again, haven't you?"

"Strangers in the night . . . married three months
and we're still strangers in the night. . ."

"I can take the rat race. It's better than letting everyone
else get all the cheese!"

"I wish you felt guilty about working, Mom. Then you could
overcompensate by spoiling me rotten."

"I've outgrown you."

"I'm new here. Where's the secretarial pool?"

"How come they're called athletes, and we're
called tomboys?"

"If you don't mind, sir, I'd rather NOT bring you luck.
I own this casino."

"That hysterical laughter in the background is
my wife—she's watching the Miss America contest."

"Only if we share all egg sitting responsibilities fifty-fifty."

"Mom—what's a housewife?"

"They laughed when I sat down to play."

"I never believed in these
boss-secretary romances before, but now
I'm awfully glad you hired me."

"Mirror, mirror on the wall...
who's the smartest of them all?"

"I'll wear the training bra, but what am I in training for?"

"Hello, my name is Howard. Which parent do you live with?"

"You told me to get all dolled up for you…"

"Does it make me look thinner?"

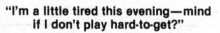

"I'm a little tired this evening—mind
if I don't play hard-to-get?"

"Don't ask me how it happened, but your wife ends up with
the business, and you get custody of
the house and children."

"For marital status you put 'Happy.'
What does *that* mean?"

"Six months ago I bought her a subscription to 'NEW WOMAN' as a joke!"

"I don't have a career; I'm a housewife. Want to make something out of it?"

"No, I don't think success makes a woman masculine, professor. Did yours make you feminine?"

"Six foot two, eyes of blue, gourmet cook, does dishes too, has anybody seen my guy?"

"If that's the way you feel, Ann, I'll get my own snack."

"I'll soon be down. I gain less every week."

"I used to be a cheerleader. Then one day I asked myself—'Why am I at the sideline cheering a bunch of boys on to victory?'"

"Sara, when are you going to get over this silly phase and come back to being a housewife?"

"You will meet a tall, dark, handsome man . . .
and go into business with his wife."

"What's fair is fair! I took a leave of absence
to HAVE him — now YOU take a
leave of absence to RAISE him!"

"Believe me, Harv, you'll get money BACK
when I tell this Morgan fella your accountant's
a dumb broad."

"Well, if it isn't the same big mouth I heard at Mimi's party
who kept saying that a woman's place is in the home!"

"It's our 'ex'..."

"She can't come out to play. She's busy nursing her new puppies...you rascal, you!"

"Well, if I'm a career girl, then you must be a career boy."

"We gotta' move with the times, Charley ... we've gotta' add a recipe section."

"Tell me...does your secretary fool around?"

"Johnson, your report is due at 3:00 sharp! Jones, I'd like
to see that invoice from the last shipment!
Cantu, take a memo....."

"When he asked me, 'Are you good in bed?' I said
'Absolutely. When I fall asleep a herd of elephants
couldn't awaken me!'"

"Jennifer! I haven't seen you since the day we were
graduated, and you and my boyfriend ran off
and got married."

"You must be new around here. That woman you called a
'broad' this morning would like a word with you
in her office!"

"My! A nice specimen of the gnaphosa
muscorum family."

"I sew, cook, iron, clean house, nurse children—yes, I am
a working woman."

"So the less expensive one ISN'T virgin wool.
Why should I care what the sheep do at night?"

"You're still in the Dark Ages, Henry. Now dub
her a knight or I will!"

"You said you wanted to hear the pitter patter
of tiny feet..."

"Remember when WE used to talk gardening
and THEY used to talk business?"

"Probably we ARE the fairer sex...
in a business sense."

"Roger! Isn't your promise to be good worth anything?"

"And this, I presume, is the little man—"

"I know, Mabel, it's lonely at the top. But it sure beats
being lonely at the bottom."

"The sudden inexplicable glee you've been feeling is
common among women reaching your time of life.
It's called the empty nest syndrome."

"It's not easy to get ahead these days.
One doesn't know whether to propose
to the boss's daughter or to the boss."

"It was wonderful! I was kicked off the team
because I'm a lousy player,
not because I'm a girl."

"Mom's having a real identity crisis. Her 'Good
Housekeeping' and 'New Woman' BOTH came today."

"That's correct. We recommend that you get a job as a
baby-sitter. That sure will discourage you from
having children in the future."

"I'll tell you what happened to that Sweet Little Girl you
thought you married! She spent 20 years with that
Sweet Little Boy she thought she married!"

"My husband and I fight all the time but we're staying
together for the sake of the animals."

"Your wife has the menu with the prices, sir. I gave you the one with the calorie count."

"YOU'RE teaching sex-ed this year? That's a laugh!"

"That's Barbara ... always a bridesmaid, never a bride ... what luck!"

"When the right woman comes along, I'll know. She'll be carrying a briefcase."

"My husband and I have a marvelous relationship. He's married to his work, and I'm married to mine."

"No, my children haven't left the nest but I have. I'm going back to school."

"Do you take this man to be your first husband?"

"It's an invitation to a divorce shower!"

"It was a friendly divorce. He took the children
and I took the corporation."

"Let's pretend we're married so we can have a fight!"

"This will tell you the names and ages of my children, where they go to school, and what my husband does. Now, may we talk about something interesting?"

"This letter in the lonely hearts column sounds just like you."

"Oh, wow! A merman!"

"The problem is our jobs...I'm head of management and he's a union official."

"I see you opening a nationwide chain of fast service beauty parlors."

"Where do unexpectant mothers report?"

"My wife, Margaret — successful producer of a four-year-old boy, a five-year-old girl, and a six-year-old TV series."

"In my day we had to marry a thing like that so we wouldn't be called an Old Maid."

"Your pad or mine?"

"I want a gal, just like the gal who hired my Dear Ol' Dad . . .!"

"What do you mean, you stopped by after work to have a few drinks with the boys?"

"No! This is NOT a retired couple. This is a retired MAN and his wife!"

"I'll bet my father has been a homemaker longer than your father."

"I can't accept this case because of conflict of interest. Opposing counsel is my wife."

"Being married for twenty years hasn't been all THAT bad—I haven't seen him for the past ten!"

"Your manuscript is superb. I think the world is ready for the story of an ugly duckling who grew up to become an ugly duck, and lived happily ever after."

"You can't live your whole life worrying about that Big Foot in the Sky coming down on you!"

"The girls and I are organizing a football team. How would you like to be our cheerleader?"

"It's not a tree house, Daddy. It's my branch office!"

". . . and so they called off the wedding, and lived happily ever after."

"I didn't believe in love at first sight, but I've certainly changed my mind! When our eyes met I knew we were made for each other, and I've been showered with love and affection ever since...I just couldn't have found a sweeter puppy!"

"Of course you have to go to college. You want to marry a professional woman, don't you?"

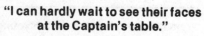

"I can hardly wait to see their faces at the Captain's table."

"So when I took over the company I discovered we didn't need quite so many male executives."

"I'm not using ANY laundry soap. I service the machines."

"I'm sorry, little girl — Santa isn't really into giving out hot stock market tips."

"The employment agency sent over the 'young chick' you asked for."

"Feel free to speak up, Hornbee—just as though you were a woman!"

"I'm sorry. My ad asking for a roommate to share my apartment should have specified MALE."

"Let's play doctor. I'll be the M.D. and you blush a lot and try to say things that will make you sound like an open-minded patient."

"...so Arthur and I decided the only solution to our problems was separate bedrooms — his in California, mine in New York."

"That minister is really good! I think I'll use her next time, too."

"What do you mean you don't make house calls? I'm your husband!"

"What's a nice girl like me doing in a place like this?????????"

"Darling, you got a raise!"

"This is what we saved by not having a baby."

"And God bless Mommy and Daddy — and
Mommy's new husband and Daddy's new wife."

"OK, Ruthie, here's a rundown of the action. A handsome
architect falls in love with a dashing, young doctor
after she performs a vasectomy on him."

"She has teeth like pearls, lips like cherries, hair like silk and a mind like a steel trap."

"Keith has the looks, the personality and muscles — but Fred, behind him, has the intelligence, is a top-notch cook, shows interest in his wife's work, and knows how to adjust to her moods."

"Well, if we go along with Mom's facts of life— I was stung by a bee."

"You may now kiss the groom."

"I was gonna get a face lift, but I figured if others can't
accept me for what I am, then phooey on them!"

"I don't want to give you a kiss
for my allowance, Daddy. I want to
take out the trash like my brother."

"You're just a dumb blond, Melvin."

"Now that you both have a job, how about
a raise in my allowance?"

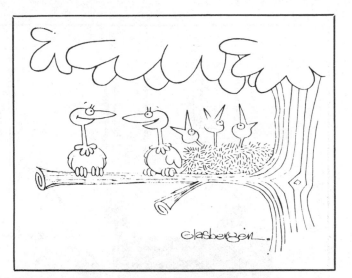

"When these kids grow up and fly away, I'm going to put my skills to good use by founding the world's first nest building service."

"The farmer takes a wife...the wife takes a job...hi-ho the dairy-o...they BOTH take the child!"

"What do you mean, *now* you know what to do?!"

LIVING TOGETHER LICENSES

"You and your suspicious mind! I'm not leaving the house.
I'm going to the bathroom!"

"It was like any other day...a few carefree
moments tidying up the place, a joyous and
fulfilling hour playing with the kids, a couple of
hours of spontaneous creativity in the kitchen..."

"In a way I suppose you could say my husband
is a good provider. He provides me with bills,
problems, headaches...and a guilt complex for
not wanting to come home after a hard day at the
office to cook dinner, wash dishes and wait on
him hand and foot."

"It pays better than mixing cake batter."

"As a candidate for the student council, I'd like to disclose a complete financial statement. I have forty-eight cents in change on hand, thirteen dollars in the bank, and a twenty-five dollar savings bond in my mother's safe deposit box."

"It lists ten additives and five preservatives, but where does it say what we're eating?

"I've been a housewife for seven years...I have five beautiful children...and I'm loving every minute of it... loving every minute of it...loving every minute of it... THAT's what I keep trying to tell myself... I'm loving every minute of it..."

"His performance almost equals mine —
taking care of six kids, a job and a house
at the same time."

"Measles, mumps and babies, please."

"I hear she's 'that kind of woman'...you know, the kind
who goes to college, gets her degree, goes to work for a
corporation and forges her way to the top..."

"My name is not TOOTS but yes I can
direct you to the president's office.
What is it you wish to see me about?"

"But after you're the first black president, the first woman president, and the youngest president, what're you going to do for kicks?"

"Good news! We've stepped up production 100 percent since we converted from man-hours to woman-hours."

"I heard Mom say you were going to fill her shoes someday — but I'm beating you to it!"

"This printing contract marks a breakthrough in cost reduction! Tell the salesman I'll see him at once!"

'Would you mind sending me to Law School instead?"

"I think it's time we had a talk about sex, too, Daddy. Shall we start with the heterosexual aspects first?"

"I've been thinking—husbands have their rights, too. Beginning tomorrow, you get to stay home with the children, and I'll go to work."

"He's the company's token male."

"Polly wants a diaphragm!"

"If only I had gotten that vasectomy one week earlier!"

"Have I found two good men for us. George and Ralph
both type ninety words per minute!"

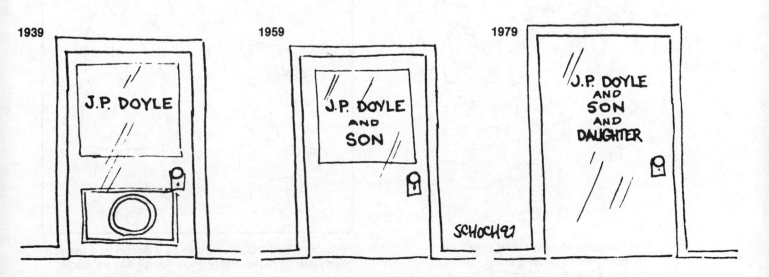

1939

1959

1979

"Yes, my intentions toward your son are honorable.
I want him to collaborate with me on a country song."

"No, I didn't change my name
when I married. Did you?"

"BIll, I'm sorry to hear about your
going into the hospital.
Is it a MALE problem?"

"Big deal! So I DON'T want to be a doctor or a lawyer!
Bodyguards make pretty good dough too, ya' know!"

"I suppose Mrs. Claus is home working herself to the bone while you sit here taking it easy!"

"You'd probably have better job prospects if you learned to type and take steno."

"Go straighten it out, Nancy. Every home needs a woman's touch!"

"I want to take you home to meet my mother. If she likes you, maybe she'll give you a job in her company."

"I'm a limited edition. I'm an only child."

"All I ever get is a peck on the cheek."

"I think she's interested in me. She asked if I've had a vasectomy."

"My wife has turned the tables on me. She now makes *me* available to all *her* visiting women friends."

"This is a very serious case. I'm afraid you're
allergic to yourself!"

"When I grow up, I'm going to stay single...
and all my children are, too!"

"No, I'm not a WOMAN doctor...
I treat both sexes!"

"That's right, I called you a BITCH! You were
bitching weren't you?"

"Why does the boy always lead? It seems to me the
better dancer should lead."

"Oh, I don't think a woman on a ship
is bad luck — especially when
she's your navigator."

"I just met some folks who consider me totally equal to a man."

"He's got an amazing figure for someone who's fathered five kids."

"My dad says that clothes make a MAN. Well, I want to be a WOMAN!"

"The way I look at it, Karen and I both clean up. While I clean up the house, she cleans up in Real Estate."

"No, darling . . . I didn't mean I wanted to CHANGE my name. I said I wanted to MAKE a name for MYSELF."

"Take good care of yourself—you belong to me..."

"I know your career means everything to you, Sylvia, but couldn't you just marry me as a hobby?"

"There's Beverly. I hear that her parents write HER for money."

"Well, if you won't let me take you out, will you take me out?"

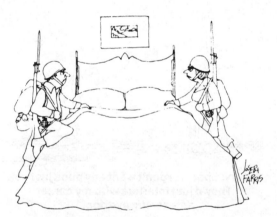

"Say AUNT!"

"This is Mr. Brown. Maybe you knew him better under Ashby, his maiden name."

"Like a damn fool I told Jane if we have any more, I'd carry them."

"Sorry, Spot . . . I don't want any pups just yet. They'd just interfere with my career as a seeing eye dog."

"Good heavens, Mother, I thought you were old enough to NO better!"

"When I first met Herbert he grew a mustache to look older. Now he is growing one to look younger."

"Dear — cold cuts and salad in the refrigerator.
Don't wait up for me. I'm going to law school.
See you in three years."

"Well, she must be SOMEBODY —
she's wearing a beeper on her belt."

"Who would have dreamed we'd be sitting here with a son
at Vassar and a daughter at West Point!"

"Would you say you're feeling (a) jealous; (b) bored; (c) unfulfilled; (d) resentful; (e) repressed; (f) desirous of change . . .?"

"Don't you remember? Twenty-four years ago today we were happily divorced!"

"Folks just don't care about us anymore, Mamma Bear. We've got to liven up our story. Next time Papa Bear orders you to make some porridge, tell him to go suck an egg."

"Of course I enjoyed myself tonight.
It was YOU I didn't enjoy."

"Daddy says you found me
on the doorstep, Mom. Doesn't he know
ANYTHING about sex?"

"This is goodbye, Elmer. NEW WOMAN has changed me!"

"Darling, I want you to meet my...er...boss."

"Are you sure your duties as a father
won't conflict with your job?"

"Read me the one where Mary had a little lamb
and she ended up owning the biggest
sheep ranch in Texas."

"Wendell, meet Marlene Bronston.
Marlene is one of the 'powers that be'."

"You'll have to excuse the mess...
I have a working husband."

"Jim, please stop acting like a man,
and just for a moment,
try being reasonable."

"Talk about beginner's luck—I'm a girl!"

"You've heard of Mother-Daughter outfits . . ."

"Frankly, Rhett, I don't give a damn whether you give a damn or not!"

"Can BOYS be doctors, Mom?"

"Mr. Baker, I've just divorced one of
'God's gifts to women.' And for the time being,
I'm returning further packages unopened."

"I'm divorcing my husband and marrying my job."

NO SEX.
NO LOVE

NO LOVE.
NO SEX

"Your crib or mine?"

"CERTAINLY I'm against hiring a woman
as vice-president of this corporation —
but it's better than letting
the competition have her!"

"Yes, John is so proud, but don't tell my husband."

"I finally found the perfect man!"

"I'm not his date...he's my date."

"The king thinks I'm funny, but the queen prefers
Carol Burnett."

"May I have the rest of the day off?
One of my kids is home sick and
my wife's job is more important than mine."

"She loves me…she loves her job…she loves me…
she loves her job…"

"When we grow up, we could have a marriage
of convenience."

"I'm leaving you for a younger man, Wendell.
I'm in my peak sexually and you're over the hill."

"Hello? Yes, this is George Swan. That's right. Helen and I
discovered a way to enjoy our careers without sacrificing
the pleasures of seeing our child grow up!"

"With Howie and me it was love at first sight.
We were BOTH too tired for sex."

"My husband has run off with another woman.
I certainly hope she's not
an industrial spy!"

"So what if Columbus discovered America.
Queen Isabella gave him the money."

"Henry, if I were the woman I am now
when we were dating, I doubt I would have
ever popped the question."

"But being a daddy isn't really a GOAL!"

"The way things are going,
by the time we're grown,
there'll be no barriers left for us to break."

"I hate it when we BOTH
have a bad day at the office."

"No, I'm not a tomboy. Are you a janegirl?"

"It's time for you to leave the nest, kiddos.
Mother has things to do."

"Well, enough about my first day on the job.
How was YOUR day, dear?"

"You're too late, kiddo! Red and I trapped the wolf and
donated it to a shelter for endangered species."

"Let's become good friends.
Let's get a divorce."

"The only time I'm gonna serve MY husband is
when we're on the tennis court!"

"Fine man you turned out to be...six tries and you
still haven't given me a daughter!"

RUTH'S
REDUCING
SALON

OUT TO LUNCH
BACK IN
150 CALORIES

LOANS

"Sorry, Freddie, but as a single male you're a bad risk.
Come back when you're married!"

"Equality is not when a female Einstein is promoted; equality is when a female Schlemiel moves ahead as fast as a male Schlemiel."

"Gee, Dad, you're lucky to have a job. All I do is hang around the house."

"Look at me when I'm talking to you!"

"Excuse me, dear. It would be rude if I didn't ask the host to dance."

"Little Red Riding Hood is a drag, Mommy.
I'd rather hear what Uncle Louie said
when he found out you were
being hired as his boss!"

"Sorry, but under our planned parenthood program
we can sell only one doll per child."

"That's what you get for not reading NEW WOMAN!"

"I'M not Slugger, that's Slugger."

"We're celebrating Nonparents' Day."

"Who says I'M going anywhere?
These are YOUR bags!"

"Why, Mom and Dad!"

"I used to be a housewife with three kids. Then one morning I woke and said to myself, 'With this kind of experience I ought to open a fast food chain.' "

"What makes you assume I'm a MAN from outer space?"

"No, of course I'm not giving up my career. As a matter of fact, I have to be back to work in about an hour."

"Did you buy this for me or did you have your secretary buy it?"

"Three queens are as good as three kings any day! We split the pot!"

"Remember—today is my day to bury bones and bark at the letter carrier, your day to lick the puppies."

"Why should I marry a good provider, Dad? I'M a good provider."

"First, I want everybody to forget that I'm a man."

"Don't ask me where she went or why . . .
all I know is that she said she was going to
pack up her troubles in her old kit bag
and smile, smile, smile."

"All day long it's clean the house,
do the laundry, change diapers,
scrub floors, cook supper . . . I wouldn't want
to be in Fred's shoes for all the money
in the world!"

Drawing by Sakren; © 1977
The New Yorker Magazine, Inc.

"Yes, I believe a woman's goal in life
should be marriage. So far
I've scored six goals!"

"You just became engaged to marry
a rich Texan? That's wonderful, son!"

"... on the contrary, I think men were destined to become homemakers.
After all, whoever heard of 'Ms. Clean' or 'Woman from Glad'?"

"You married your secretary? So did I."

"Sure I'll be your girl...and you can be my boy!"

"An olive or onion, honey?"

"I want 100 shares of Xerox, 100 shares of IBM
and 100 shares of IT&T."

"When I leave home, Mom's turning my room
into a briefcase."

"You're absolutely right—enough about you!"

"Frankly, I owe all my success to a man—
he gave me a divorce."

"They make a perfect couple...He's a doctor and she's a
malpractice attorney!"

"You presume wrong."

"Yes, men have helped my career in business...
I learned by THEIR mistakes!"

"You scratch my back, Sarah,
and I'll scratch yours."

"OK, guys, since I'm not sure who's the father, I'm giving
each one of you a pick of the litter."

"I've discovered this MARVELOUS little market—
the Stock Market!"

"Now that you're a career woman, Jessie,
I suppose you'll be asserting yourself
a lot more now, and if you care to exploit
me sexually, I'll understand."

"It's OK, sir, it's been taken care of."

"After my brother and I were born, my mother
had my father fixed, too."

"Maybe your daddy is bigger than my daddy, but I'll bet he
doesn't have half the earning capacity as my mommy!"

"Why should my husband mind if I work?
I don't mind if he works."

"Now, remember this about the birds and bees, dear.
BOTH are equal partners."

"No, I'm not happily married.
I'm happily single."

"My parents wanted me to be a good wife
to a successful man. I decided to be a
successful woman to a good husband."

"You want a DIVORCE for Christmas!
Let's discuss this later, dear."

"If you're just going to sit around, why don't you
sit on the EGGS?"

"Sounds like a fun night, but do I have to
marry the Prince?"

"Jack and Jill went up the hill to get a pail of water.
Jack fell down and broke his crown—and Jill bandaged
it up and later became a famous doctor."

"I not only care what my KIDS are going to do when THEY grow up. I also want to know what I'M going to do when I grow up."

"No, I want auto mechanics. He gets the needlepoint!"

"You would be ill-advised to give me a piece of your mind!!! You need every little bit you've got."

"Poor Helen will be so relieved to see me. I left her a gag
note this morning saying I was leaving her!"

"I had previous experience—climbing walls!"

"Congratulations, Lola, We just voted you into our club."

"I'm spending the evening by myself, Ralph . . . and in good company I might add."

"Oh, give me land, lots of land, I can sell or I can lease...don't fence me in..."

"I'm not PLAYING hard to get, Phillip . . .
I AM hard to get."

"Herbert, we've got to stop meeting like this."

"We have two serious problems in living together—
his wife and my husband!"

"I always cry at my mother's weddings."

"When you say you want to speak to my parents, do you mean my mommy and her new husband, or daddy and his new wife or my mommy and daddy?"

"No, there aren't any king bees."

"Well, Dad, since you arranged my marriage,
I thought it was only natural to see you
about planning my divorce!"

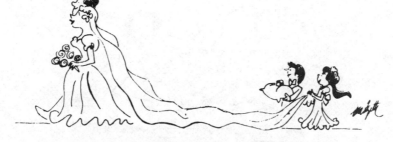

"I knew our open marriage would work, Paul.
I have a date tonight, too!"

"Yes, I think my fiance's mother approves of me.
Yesterday she bought 100 shares
of my company's stock."

"...and this one's by a previous marriage."

"When the magic went out of my marriage,
I divorced my husband, got a job
and found magic in my work."

"You two, stop that!"

"Gloria, remember my saying there wasn't
a man on earth I'd marry?"

"That'll be 37¢ for the new 'thingamagig'
and $27.50 for knowing where
to put it."

"It's really amazing how a silly little piece of paper
could bring us so much happiness, and strengthen
our relationship and understanding toward
one another. I'm glad we got the divorce, Ronald."

"I must have forgotten to water the plants."

"My mom does creative work, my dad does creative work. I just create work."

"Do you realize, Walter, that there are 40 pounds of you I'm not legally married to?"

"I'm supposed to get married next week, Ms. Clayburn.
Pencil that into my schedule."

"Oh, I just love to give gifts that I make myself.
That's why I always give money."

"Did Little Miss Muffet actually like
that curds and whey goop, or was it a
publicity stunt to advertise
her dairy company?"

"I know what they see in her! She's brilliant,
rich and a corporation president."

"Now that my mom's getting a new husband, I wonder
whether I can get a new brother."

"Sure, I'll tell you why *I'm* taking care of you.
Your mother wised up."

"You're sneaky! You're being
rational while I'm being emotional!"

"See Jane run. See Dick run. See Jane beat Dick in the 10th congressional district."

"I've got to go to the bathroom. Can I count on you not to take over the kingdom?"

"It wasn't *thinking* like a man that got me where I am today. It was *out*-thinking a man!"

"You're an ugly, stupid ass, but I love you anyway."

"In case it slipped your mind, Oswald, I'm STILL a consenting adult!"

"You prefer to serve only men in this bar? Fine! Make mine witty, strong and handsome!"

"I don't have to put up with all your 'bitching'…I'm going home to my husband!"

"You'll get ready for your date AFTER working hours, Bradford!!!"

"Oh, yes, I KNEW there was something I forgot to tell you. I filed for divorce today."

"Your dad cannot beat up my dad because your dad is now my dad, remember!"

"I liked the way you dispatched that bully without, even for a moment, losing your femininity."

"No, I don't have a headache. I'm not going to make excuses anymore. I just don't want to."

"Now that I have a job,
I'm no longer Frank's *bitter* half."

"If I were the miller's daughter, I would have spun the straw into gold, sold it on the open market and used the money to buy my own business."

"We'll think it over."

"But, Mr. Deiter, I *did* run out for coffee and a sweet roll!
It was delicious, thank you."

"Why, you ask? I'll tell you why.
I was getting good and sick of
'How's the little woman!' "

"I don't care if it's constitutional or not—
I say a prayer before every test."

"Do you promise to love, cherish and remain
on good speaking terms after divorce?"

"We have a special rate if you want it for just an hour."

"Gee, Mom, when will I be old enough to get a divorce?"

"Why yes, I AM the former Sarah Mason . . .
and the PRESENT Sarah Mason."

"My class just voted me 'Most Likely to Marry
a Successful Woman'!"

"I see your book is about how women should be content to stay home and look after their children. So, why aren't you at home taking care of yours?"

"Well, what did we learn at school tonight?"

"My wife and I have learned a lot these past few years. Martha's learned to be independent and I've learned to accept it."

"Meet my husband, the BREADwinner. I pay for everything else."

"Congratulations, Mom, you're a grandmother. . .I just became a PARENT company."

"Mom, Dad, I've been thinking...perhaps a new bicycle, some extra spending money, and a nice stereo in my room would help me bear up under the overwhelming strain and trauma of your impending divorce."

"Frankly, I've been expecting you."

"Since I landed that good position, he gives a bigger hoot for my booty than he does for my body!"

"Now tell me about your relationship with your father."

"OK, Mr. Higby. You've sold me on my great big baby
blues, but you haven't sold me on your product."

"But if Mommy isn't a carpenter, how come
she's always going to board meetings?"

"Twelve years of marriage and the closest he ever
brought me to that big 'O,' was the balance
column of our checking account."

"I don't quite understand. . .according to these records,
you've had one more divorce than you've had marriages."

"Eberhardt, say something sexually aggressive to me."

"You're wasting your time, sir. We're working out our divorce settlement."

"She wants the head of the house!"

"She's been like this ever since the kids went away to school."

"Dad, Janet and I are getting a divorce and I'm going home to Mom. . .would you happen to know who she's living with?"

"I owe my career to my husband who inspired me with these words: 'As long as I pay the bills around here, you will do what I say.' "

"I'm bored. Let's fight."

"Isn't this a fun way to watch our figures?"

"No, no. We didn't put granny into a nursing *home;* she put herself into a nursing *school.*"

"As a single parent, I can't put you all through college, so why don't you all get jobs and help put *me* through college?"

"Sugar and spice and everything nice?! What am I,
a woman or a cupcake?"

"This is Morton, my future ex-husband."

"To us and the shambles we've made of our lives."

Drawing by H. Martin; ©1978
The New Yorker Magazine, Inc.

"Fix me a martini like my relationship: On the rocks."

"I didn't mind your bringing your work HOME with you, but…"

"Of course you've met me somewhere before.
I'm your ex-wife's attorney — remember?"

"But I don't want a little white cottage with a picket fence.
I want a big manufacturing plant with a security fence!"

"Weber, the way to a man's heart is *not*
through his stomach; it's through his
upper chest canal!"

"Yes, I'm an only child. Are you an only husband?"

CATHY'S DETECTIVE AGENCY
WE PRY HARDER

"You're straightforward, honest, practical and ambitious.
That's what I like about you, Bradford...
you THINK like a woman!!"

"Let's see . . . that's $20 per hour for the magic,
plus $15 for the hairdo, and
$10 for the manicure . . ."

"The doctor wasn't really praising you when she said you have great retentive powers. She was telling you you're constipated."

"I'm working on a screenplay, too. I call it *Blondes Prefer Gentlemen*."

"Is it true blondes have more funds?"

"And what can I do for *you* today?"

"Well, so much for 'Europe on $10.00 a day'."

"I'm looking for that fifth doctor
who won't recommend what
four out of five doctors recommend."

"Haven't you heard of birth control?"

"Polly wants her rights!"

"Frank, this is Jack Kurtz.
Jack is tonight's guest host."

"So you'd swim the deepest ocean and climb the highest
mountain. But would you get neutered?"

"So this is reconciliation."

"Of course I believe in trial marriages.
Better the trial is before than after."

"We'll be in when we're through playing 'house.'
We're getting our divorce now."

"Mom, this is Chubby.
I invited her to spend the night with me."

"Sure we had the pill in the 1940's—I married one!"

"I wish we could go back to the way we were *before* marriage—complete strangers!!!"

"It's been nice chatting with you, Loretta, and remember me to the little man."

"Now I'm both a mother-in-law and a woman in law."

"Mommy, if you're the bride-to-be, and he's the groom-to-be, does that make me the child-to-be?"

"It's been very refreshing having lunch with a female client...men squirm so when I pick up the check."

"... unfortunately, they did not live happily ever after. In fact shortly after their first anniversary they began to really get on each other's nerves. So they got divorced."

"Never bank on your beauty, Barbie. Had I invested in my looks, I'd be bankrupt by now!"

"Charlie found the secret to success...
he married his boss!"

"I get real depressed, knowing that someday,
this could all belong to me."

"I'm trying to put on weight now,
so when I grow up it'll be easy
to keep my girlish figure."

"You're right, Doctor, you don't have to be
a chicken to know eggs ... but have you
ever tried *laying* one?!"

"I met the new girl on the block,
and she's teaching me some new punches."

"We've been married less than a month. I wish you'd stop introducing me as your first husband."

"If someone should happen to ask what I see in you, what should I tell them?"

"When I was growing up, I faced almost constant ridicule because my last name was Quigglewiggle. So when Susan Greene and I got married, I jumped at the chance to change my name!"

"Martin and I had a trial separation,
and it worked out so well,
we're getting a divorce."

"I feel a bit masochistic today, Harry.
Let's get married."

"C'mon...easy, Carol. There was just no way he could
know we out-rank him."

"Your executive retreat or mine?"

"I'm not a divorcée . . . I'm a divorcor."

"Why don't you make Romeo and Juliet a real tragedy, Mr. Shakespeare? Have them live and get married."

"When I grow up, I'm not going to Europe until I can say 'no' in all languages."

"Well, I don't need a face-lift half as bad as you need a body-lift!"

"For years, Berkely, you've been the dominant element in our marriage. You bestowed upon yourself a strict father image, and I learned to act like a nice little girl. But you overlooked one thing: Little girls always grow up — some later than others. And when little girls grow up, they no longer need to live with their daddies."

"Mr. Dumbkauf, you think a woman shouldn't be President because her menstrual cycle would make her act crazy and want to declare war on somebody? Gee, I'm in my cycle now — as are millions of other women. Can you explain why we're not all out in the street stabbing, shooting and setting fire to people?"

"Admit it. You're only after me for my mind."

"Here's to 'whoops!!!' breaking up!!!"

"What you're proposing is bigamy! I'm already married to my job."

"You seem to be a bit confused over the expression 'performance in bed'."

"What's so strange about my editing a man's magazine?
Men have edited women's magazines for ages, and no one
seems to think that strange."

"I've decided to come out of the closet.
I *like* being a housewife."

"So that there won't be any misunderstanding,
these trial papers are the only briefs
you're going to see tonight."

"What we have here is a
marriage of convenience!!!"

"The glamour of living alone as a divorced man is
beginning to tarnish."

"We don't need sex education in our schools! A song I
heard on the radio this afternoon told me more than I
probably should know at this time!!"

"For a woman with a headache—you're a helluva
human dynamo!"

"I once discovered how to create life in a test tube, but I
destroyed the records. Why spoil everybody's fun?"

"Don't worry, Geraldine, computers will never
replace us reporters — click —
reporters — click — reporters —."

"We're not planning to use it, but it's great for keeping
our marriage on its toes."

"Of course, you've met me somewhere before.
I'm your TV repairwoman—remember?!"

"You don't need another drink. What you need
is a good cry."

"But if we got married,
you'd expect me to move IN!"

"Sorry, but I prefer to remain footloose and
fiance-free!"

"I wish you hadn't confessed to being a married man—
now I suppose I have to tell you about my husband..."

"Going to singles bars is like
digging in the garden —
you keep running into clods!"

"Well, men get headaches too, you know..."

"Walter and I went to Acapulco to find each other.
Then I found Ellen and he found Roger!"

"When I think of all the afternoons our club
wasted playing bridge."

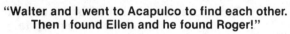

"Say 'Oink'."

"Do you know 'I'm gonna wash that man right out
of my hair'?"

"This is my daughter, Mary; and this is Ed,
my living-together-in-law."

"Are you an Old Lady, a Lib Woman
or a New Woman?"

"Sure I love you and I'm willing to accept
that my wife has worked herself up to
an office position superior to mine.
But you must realize that it's not easy
calling you 'Boss' by day and
'Poopsie' by night."

"If you don't get a divorce for your own sakes, how about
getting one for my sake?"

"I'd call him a dope, except that he's not the least
bit habit forming."

"But Julia . . . You *can't* leave me . . .
You're only going to prove my ex-wife right
when she says I'm impossible to live with!!!"

"It's too bad you're divorced, Mr. Forbes. We don't issue
credit cards to single men."

"Personnel sent it over in answer to your 'Hire me a cupcake' order."

"If you don't do your homework, how do you expect to grow up to be rich and influential like mommy?"

"My roommate wants me to be Best Woman at his wedding."

"Since our divorce, I've discovered I didn't lose the best years of my life to you. I'm just finding them *now*!"

"I guess you're right, Howard. It is a man's world... violence, unemployment, pollution..."

"I don't want to put you on the spot, but do you think your living arrangement will last long enough to invest in a bike for me?"

"...And who gives this MAN in marriage?"

"Now let me get this straight. We're *all* here researching a book?"

"Am I glad you're not one of those New Women!"

"Jennifer and I raced home. She was next to last and I was second."

"Say, why don't we have
separate honeymoons!"

"I guess it's a sign of the times."

"My husband says my becoming a New Woman is
turning him into an old man..."

"Some day, if things continue the way they are, all this will be yours."

"That's in case I forget later."

"It's a JILL in the box…"

"But the nightmare is not that I dream my husband left me. The nightmare is that I wake up and he's still there!"

"Whatever happened to that sweet little
girl I married?"

"Remember the Mouton Rothschild I put away
for a special occasion? Well this is it…
I'm leaving you!"

"Do you think as woman such as yourself — who has all the qualities of a
topflight executive — could see it clear to work outside the home
in order to make enough money to raise my allowance?"

"Susan, you should accept yourself as you are. Besides,
I need my tennis balls."

"I get weary making meals for you every day.
Can't you eat out some of the time
and give me a rest?"

"Sure. I'll play cowboys with you! I'll be the sheriff
and you be the sweet, wholesome rancher's son
who keeps hoping I'll ask him to marry me!"

"Cause my wife's gone back to work, that's why!"

"Wow! Lighter fluid works better than brandy."

"Dear Albert: Last night you asked me what had happened to the 'sweet little chick' you married. I thought about that remark a lot and here's the answer: She has flown the coop."

"She's a working mother and I'm a working father."

"Well, I don't like to promise, but I'll try."

DUE TO AIR POLLUTION THIS HISTORIC VIEW HAS BEEN CANCELLED.

"You really think so? That makes two of us!"

"I'll have the Businesswoman's Special."

"Hold your horses, Fairy Godmother. The only thing the Prince and I have in common is an interest in ballroom dancing. I don't think that's a very solid foundation on which to build a happy relationship."

"I've decided to go on a 40-hour week."

"But I don't WANT a playhouse...I want a play-factory!"

"Someday my princess will come along, and then I'll live happily ever after."

"But gee, hon, you're my wife. Why would you want to be a county commissioner?"

"Well, you said you wanted to make love in the worst way...and you did...you did..."

"The answer is NO, Bill...No; N-O, not so, as opposed to yes, used in expressions of refusal or denial..."

"Sorry I'm late—the board meeting ran over."

"You REALLY want to know what the moonlight, salt air and lapping waves makes me think about? It makes me think this would be a fantastic site for me to build a vacation resort!"

"My mommy's an equal opportunity employer— she hires men."

"I don't know, turtle oil never stopped ME from wrinkling."

"It says 'Happy Valentine's Day.
Love, Shirley'!"

"Our company is looking for a man with drive, a man with
foresight, a man with courage, a man who isn't afraid to
say his wife is president of the company he works for..."

"Let me put it this way. I am not the woman
I used to be. Therefore, I am not the same woman
you married 20 years ago. Therefore, the couple
we once were is no longer. Therefore, since
the couple who married 20 years ago does not exist,
neither does our marriage. Therefore, goodbye."

"What wine goes with a New Woman?"

"Take me away from all of this, Frank. Divorce me."

"You mean your parents never told you about
being a New Woman?"

"Jack and Jill went up the hill, to fetch
a pail of water. Jack fell down and broke his crown
and Jill completed the assignment
and won the everlasting gratitude
and respect of her employer."

"We aren't married...we're just living together."

"What's the matter, Mac?...
Haven't you ever seen
a man with long hair before?!"

"Ball schmall! I wanna go to LAW SCHOOL!"

"Goldilocks seems to have tried out a lot of beds for size. Was she on the pill?"

"You keep telling me to be sensible, Henry, so I'm going to be. I'm leaving you."

"It's so nice to be of a species that's so ecologically essential."

"Do you realize, Frank, that this is the first thing we've done together in five years?"

"Looks as if we're in for an office party. The president of the company just became a mother!"

"So this woman came up to me at a party
and asked me to tell her all about myself.
How was I to know she was
the District Attorney?"

"Get married? Are you kidding?! It's going to be hard
enough adjusting to just ONE new person in my life!"

"Sex isn't all THAT good. It turns you into a parent."

"Well, if it isn't Herbie Lewis from high school —
the guy who used to call me
'that dumb broad who thinks
she's as smart as a man'!"

"What's wrong with us, Mason?
Everyone we know has been divorced
at least once but us!"

"They were roommates at college."

"I'm Mrs. Russell Harris and this is my husband, Mr. Shirley Harris."

"Of course, my boyfriend believes in marriage. He's married!"

"Like WOW! . . . That was a CLOSE one! . . .
ME about to arrest YOU for
loitering-for-the-purposes-of-prostitution
and YOU about to pull ME in as a
vagrant-with-suspicion-of-possession!
We'd NEVER have lived THAT down
at the precinct!"

"Yes, Gosgrove, they still talk about you in the office,
when you said, 'Before I take orders from a woman,
I'll go beg in the streets!'"

"No I'm not looking for a husband! I'm looking for a cream
cheese without olives on it."

"Oh, we've met.
We were once married to one another."

"Don't you ever get tired of playing house?"

"Boy, what I wouldn't give to be six hundred again!"

"I love him...I love him not..."

"Suzy, old girl, I think it's time you and I had a woman
to woman talk..."

"Dad, be honest! After visiting with me for a week, do you still think your little plain Jane is a lonely spinster?"

"It's a new plot: boy meets girl, girl meets girl."

"I believe in planned parenthood. Sometimes I wish I could have planned mine."

"Mary, Mary, reasonably contrary, how does your factory grow?"

"You say your wife doesn't understand you? Here's my card. Call my secretary for an appointment and we'll talk about it. I'm a psychiatrist."

"Only if we agree to support each other financially while he or she is going to law school and share all household and child care responsibilities fifty-fifty."

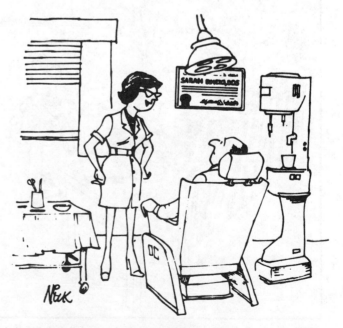

"Let's hope I have better luck with your teeth than you had with my car."

VANSELOW

"I earned it. Your father cooked it. Now eat it!"

"Things are looking up. She took down John Travolta's picture and put up Patricia Harris's."

"Yes, my husband does make a lot of money...in fact, I pay ALL of my employees well."

"I'd like to invest my money in those corporations wise enough to have women in high executive positions."

"Oh, hell, I think I love you!"

"Take me to your leader—whoever she is."

"This is just the beginning, Caroline! Someday there'll be a big city here, chock full of people pushing an' robbing an' killing an' . . ."

"Mr. Hays, my husband doesn't understand me."

"What would you say if I told you that you're the fifth man to propose to me since I became president of the company?"

"I think there must be something wrong with me. I just felt like kissing Jimmy instead of punching him in the nose."

"For a husband and wife who manage rival companies they get along remarkably well."

"Mom, is pregnancy hereditary?"

"Well, that's all very interesting, Mom, but what I'd REALLY like to know is how babies AREN'T made."

"Last night I dreamed you and I were consenting adults!"

"You're sitting in his chair."

"I've been happily divorced from the same man for nearly five years."

"Our daughter would like to go to work for your company. Do you mind if she just digs in and takes the bull by the horn . . .?"

"My mother wanted me to marry a doctor, but it was so much easier to become one than to live with one."

"The answer is NO, Bill…No; N-O, not so, as opposed to yes, used in expressions of refusal or denial…"

"Sorry I'm late—the board meeting ran over."

"You REALLY want to know what the moonlight, salt air and lapping waves makes me think about? It makes me think this would be a fantastic site for me to build a vacation resort!"

"My mommy's an equal opportunity employer— she hires men."

"I don't know, turtle oil never stopped ME from wrinkling."

"It says 'Happy Valentine's Day.
Love, Shirley'!"

"Our company is looking for a man with drive, a man with
foresight, a man with courage, a man who isn't afraid to
say his wife is president of the company he works for..."

"Let me put it this way. I am not the woman
I used to be. Therefore, I am not the same woman
you married 20 years ago. Therefore, the couple
we once were is no longer. Therefore, since
the couple who married 20 years ago does not exist,
neither does our marriage. Therefore, goodbye."

"What wine goes with a New Woman?"

"Take me away from all of this, Frank. Divorce me."

"You mean your parents never told you about being a New Woman?"

"Jack and Jill went up the hill, to fetch a pail of water. Jack fell down and broke his crown and Jill completed the assignment and won the everlasting gratitude and respect of her employer."

"We aren't married...we're just living together."

"What's the matter, Mac?...
Haven't you ever seen
a man with long hair before?!"

"Ball schmall! I wanna go to LAW SCHOOL!"

"Goldilocks seems to have tried out a lot of beds for size. Was she on the pill?"

"You keep telling me to be sensible, Henry, so I'm going to be. I'm leaving you."

"It's so nice to be of a species that's so ecologically essential."

"Do you realize, Frank, that this is the first thing we've done together in five years?"

"Looks as if we're in for an office party. The president of the company just became a mother!"

"So this woman came up to me at a party and asked me to tell her all about myself. How was I to know she was the District Attorney?"

"Get married? Are you kidding?! It's going to be hard enough adjusting to just ONE new person in my life!"

"Sex isn't all THAT good. It turns you into a parent."

"Well, if it isn't Herbie Lewis from high school — the guy who used to call me 'that dumb broad who thinks she's as smart as a man'!"

"What's wrong with us, Mason? Everyone we know has been divorced at least once but us!"

"They were roommates at college."

"I'm Mrs. Russell Harris and this is my husband,
Mr. Shirley Harris."

"Of course, my boyfriend believes in
marriage. He's married!"

"Like WOW! . . . That was a CLOSE one! . . .
ME about to arrest YOU for
loitering-for-the-purposes-of-prostitution
and YOU about to pull ME in as a
vagrant-with-suspicion-of-possession!
We'd NEVER have lived THAT down
at the precinct!"

"Yes, Gosgrove, they still talk about you in the office,
when you said, 'Before I take orders from a woman,
I'll go beg in the streets!'"

"No I'm not looking for a husband! I'm looking for a cream
cheese without olives on it."

"Oh, we've met.
We were once married to one another."

"Don't you ever get tired of playing house?"

"Boy, what I wouldn't give to be six hundred again!"

"I love him…I love him not…"

"Suzy, old girl, I think it's time you and I had a woman
to woman talk…"

"Dad, be honest! After visiting with me for a week, do you still think your little plain Jane is a lonely spinster?"

"It's a new plot: boy meets girl, girl meets girl."

"I believe in planned parenthood. Sometimes I wish I could have planned mine."

"Mary, Mary, reasonably contrary, how does your factory grow?"

"You say your wife doesn't understand you? Here's my card. Call my secretary for an appointment and we'll talk about it. I'm a psychiatrist."

"Only if we agree to support each other financially while he or she is going to law school and share all household and child care responsibilities fifty-fifty."

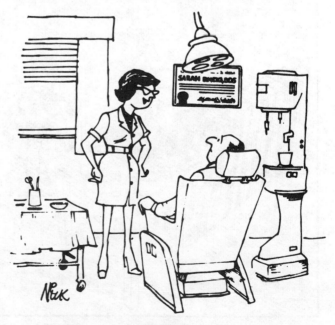

"Let's hope I have better luck with your teeth than you had with my car."

VANSELOW

"I earned it. Your father cooked it. Now eat it!"

"Things are looking up. She took down John Travolta's picture and put up Patricia Harris's."

"Yes, my husband does make a lot of money...in fact, I pay ALL of my employees well."

"I'd like to invest my money in those corporations wise
enough to have women in high executive positions."

"Oh, hell, I think I love you!"

"Take me to your leader—whoever she is."

"This is just the beginning, Caroline!
Someday there'll be a big city here,
chock full of people pushing an'
robbing an' killing an' . . ."

"Mr. Hays, my husband doesn't understand me."

"What would you say if I told you that you're the fifth man to propose to me since I became president of the company?"

"I think there must be something wrong with me. I just felt like kissing Jimmy instead of punching him in the nose."

"For a husband and wife who manage rival companies they get along remarkably well."

"Mom, is pregnancy hereditary?"

"Well, that's all very interesting, Mom, but what I'd REALLY like to know is how babies AREN'T made."

"Last night I dreamed you and I were consenting adults!"

"You're sitting in his chair."

"I've been happily divorced from the same man for nearly five years."

"Our daughter would like to go to work for your company. Do you mind if she just digs in and takes the bull by the horn . . .?"

"My mother wanted me to marry a doctor, but it was so much easier to become one than to live with one."

"When I grow up I'm going to be a movie director, and feature a smart blonde woman with a dumb blond man."

"21-7/8's for your thoughts, dear."

"If we let her play, she'll win all our marbles. So let's just tell her she can't play because she's a girl."

"Yes, we have met somewhere before, but it wasn't in Spain, Paris OR Rio...it was in the reception room of your office where I was being hired as your replacement."

"I'd go home to Mother if I knew who she was living with!"

"I couldn't ask for a better husband.
He's cute, he's smart, he's talented,
he's DEDUCTIBLE . . ."

"That again for dinner?"

"I hope you aren't relying too heavily on ME to make you a grandmother."

"Years ago, if you had asked me for my 'dream' person, I would've said tall, sexy, witty, athletic and the head of a multinational corporation. Little did I realize I'd be describing myself."

"I'm the Old Maid...thank goodness!!"

"Next week will be our first anniversary, and John is giving me something I've wanted for months — a divorce."

"...to love, cherish, and not get upset if she earns more than you do..."

"...so one day I up and said to myself, 'Violet,' I said, 'STOP SHRINKING!'"

"We're compatible—between spats."

"Behind every successful woman there's a man. Would you like to be that man?"

"Little Miss Muffet sat on a tuffet eating her curds and whey. Along came a spider and sat down beside her, and that got her interested in entomology."

"We're trying to figure out how to tell our father that
his son flunked auto mechanics and his
daughter made an 'A.'"

"Hello, Marsha? Have I got marvelous news! My son
is marrying a doctor!"

"Yes, I'm a 'lady' lawyer. I understand
you're a 'gentleman' dentist."

"Wow! She IS a real doctor!"

"If we get a divorce, will you still do my income taxes for me?"

"That was a cute little song, Dad. However, if I were Mrs. Bailey, I would have told Bill to go fiddle his Aries and left it at that."

"Until we studied Russia, I didn't realize I live in a police state at home."

"Hello, Nancy W. Parsons, marriage counselor? This is an emergency. Can we meet you at your office in fifteen minutes?"

"I want to be a secretary when I grow up— Secretary of State!"

"I'll marry you if you'll support me while I go through law school."

"Good morning, Mr. Grimes. I'm Dr. Potter and this is Nurse Brown."

"No, I wouldn't exactly say Ellen was upset when I said I was leaving her . . ."

"I think I've been a good little girl, but I don't stay home helping my mother clean house. I go to work on my paper route."

"Where am I NOT supposed to hit HER . . . below the belt or above the belt?"

"They are so young to be getting a divorce. It probably won't last."

"You'll like the doctor. She speaks from experience."

"So when I said that no wife of mine was going to set up her own business, she agreed. That's when she got the divorce."

"He just lost a long legal battle over custody of the children. He had to take them."

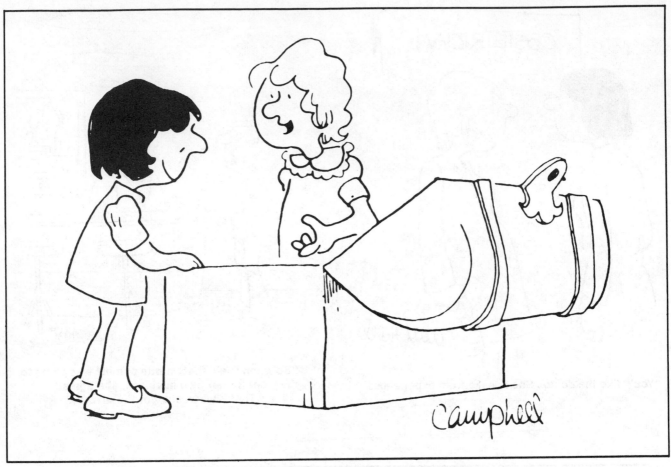

"This is my hope chest. So far, I have a stethoscope, a prescription pad and an appointment book."

"He assumed that because I was a woman I liked to be dominated. He's now aware of another myth about women!"

"... boxing gloves, a baseball glove, a firewoman's hat, a doctor's kit ..."

"I'm paying. I'll taste the wine."

"This is a TV first, J.B. a female quarterback doing a shaving commercial."

"And then the prince had a vasectomy and they lived happily ever after."

"Your résumé is impressive, but I'm afraid conflicts might arise because of your responsibilities as a husband and father."

"That rumor is true. The president of our company is EXTREMELY effeminate."

"Yes, I'm a working woman. Are you a working man?"

"No, they're not married, just living together."

"Then it's settled. January through June it's a Kingdom, and July through December, it's a Queendom!"

"Mom, here's your sack of gumdrops. It's your reward for getting good grades."

"You seem confused. I'm not one of the
'girls from the office.' I'm a woman.
Are these the boys from the sales force?"

"Why do you need an "A" in the course?
You'll probably marry an ambitious woman
who'll make a good life for you."

"It's not fair; every time we play, she gets
to be Chris Evert."

"It's MY letter sweater!
THAT'S whose letter sweater
it is!"

". . . and to think this merger would
never have happened had we not
met that day at the beauty salon."

"Your wish has come true, Momma.
I'm marrying a lawyer. We're going to
set up practice together."

"Take off your clothes and stop worrying. To me you're
just a patient, not a man."

"Let's play house. You be the daughter. I'll be the mommy,
and Roddy, here, can be my ex."

"Do you have something for the woman
on her way up?"

"I don't mind being referred to as a homemaker.
I own the Acme Construction Company."

"Of course you remember me, Jennings. I'm that upstart secretary you fired a few years ago because I refused to ask for a promotion on my back."

"You're right, I *have* slept around to get where I am today. I've slept in planes, on trains, and once I was so exhausted after a big sales meeting that I even fell asleep in a taxi!"

"Do you have any idea how embarrassing it is to sit on an adopted egg for six weeks, only to find you've been trying to hatch a pair of panty hose?"